J.C.F. BACH
MUSICAL LEISURE HOU

Edited by Timothy Roberts

THE ASSOCIATED BOARD OF
THE ROYAL SCHOOLS OF MUSIC

INTRODUCTION

Johann Christoph Friedrich Bach (1732–95) was the third of the four sons of J.S. Bach to achieve renown as composers in their own right. He was taught by his father and then by his cousin, Johann Elias Bach. Shortly before Sebastian's death in 1750 the young Friedrich entered the service of the small but enlightened court at Bückeburg, a post that he was to retain for the rest of his life. In 1778 he visited his younger brother Johann Christian in London; he was favourably impressed by English grand pianos, and took one back to Germany with him. In addition to performing other composers' works, including operas by Mozart and Gluck, the 'Bückeburg Bach' wrote symphonies, concertos and chamber music in a forward-looking Italian style, and like his brothers he enjoyed a wide reputation as a keyboard virtuoso.

In 1787–8 J.C.F. Bach published a four-volume collection of his keyboard music, songs and cantatas under the title *Musikalische Nebenstunden* ('Musical Leisure Hours'). The present selection has been made from the 69 short keyboard pieces in the anthology; they are miniatures intended for light entertainment, and perhaps also as didactic pieces for the flourishing amateur market. Many are in popular dance forms of the day such as the minuet, angloise (contredanse), Schwaebisch (Swabian dance), villanella, musette and march. A few look back to the style, and even the thematic material, of J.S. Bach's Two-part Inventions (see Nos.8, 20, 23 and 24), while the Solfeggio in D (No.4) is reminiscent of both the C major and B-flat major Preludes in Book One of the '48'. J.C.F. Bach's mature style is seen at its best in the Andante in G (No.19), Adagio in C minor (No.25) and Menuet in A (No.26).

The editor of music of this period is faced with the problem that, unlike the continuous legato taught as basic today, mid-18th-century keyboard touch was based on a non-legato in which many notes were held for only half their notated length. Staccato dots or wedges indicated an even more detached style, while sustained, legato touch was normally only used for slurred notes or where *tenuto* was specified. In this edition some editorial suggestions for articulation have been added, though to indicate the touch appropriate to every note would result in a confusing and over-edited text. In the absence of any indication to the contrary, a lightly articulated touch should be assumed.

The composer's dynamics have been supplemented in some pieces, but the player is left to add the finer shadings essential to a musical performance. The ornament realisations printed small above the stave are based on the composer's own instructions in *Musikalische Nebenstunden*, which are in turn selected from C.P.E. Bach's famous *Essay* of 1753.* Some of the ornaments are difficult to play lightly on the relatively heavy action of a modern piano, especially the trilled turn ∾, which may sometimes be replaced by a plain turn ∾ or even omitted altogether.

Editorial additions to the original are distinguished by small type or square brackets. Editorial slurs are printed as ⌒ or (where a piece originally had no slurs) specified in a footnote. Original indications of staccato are printed in their original form as wedges, while all staccato dots are editorial. (The two signs normally had the same meaning at this time.) Commas indicating phrase-endings are also editorial; a bracketed comma indicates a small articulation within the phrase.

TIMOTHY ROBERTS
London 1987

*For an outline of the north German style of ornamentation, see the Introduction to Howard Ferguson's edition of *C.P.E. Bach: Selected Keyboard Works* (4 vols., Associated Board).

MUSICAL LEISURE HOURS

J.C.F. BACH

All dynamics are editorial.

AB 2008

[♩ = c.100]

MENUET in F

6

MENUET in C

[non legato]

All slurs are editorial.

[2 da volta: poco rit.]

[♩ = c.120]

SOLFEGGIO in D
[Allegro moderato]

et sim.

AB 2008

All dynamics are editorial.

[♩ = c.54]

MARCHE in G
[Allegretto]

*Undotted quavers in the original (but compare bar 39).

ANGLOISE in D

*The bracketed notes may be omitted by players with small hands.

12

ALLEGRETTO in D

All slurs and dynamics are editorial.   *Original reading:

AB 2008

ANGLOISE in A

[Vivace]

All slurs are editorial.

[♩ = c.138]

ALLEGRO in E flat

10

All slurs and dynamics are editorial.

[♩ = c.96]

SOLFEGGIO in G

All slurs and dynamics are editorial.

[♩ = c.52]

AB 2008

ALLEGRO in E minor

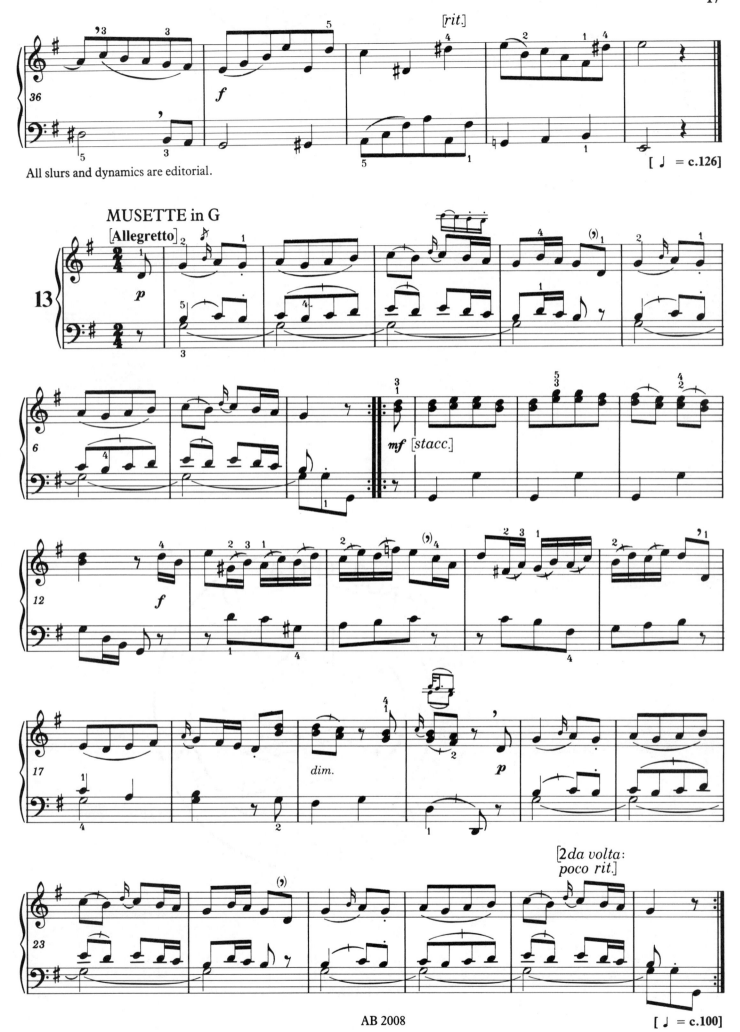

[rit.]

36

f

All slurs and dynamics are editorial.

[♩ = c.126]

MUSETTE in G

13

[Allegretto]

p

6

mf [stacc.]

12

f

17

dim.

p

[2da volta: poco rit.]

23

[♩ = c.100]

SCHERZO in C

*Suggested simplification:

AB 2008

★ SCHWAEBISCH in F

[Vivace]

*Swabian Dance, or Ländler.
All slurs and dynamics are editorial.

AB 2008

ANGLOISE in D

[Allegretto]

mf

[stacc. sempre]

f

Trio [Poco meno mosso]

mf

p [dolce]
[ten.]

Fine

[ten.]

mp

[ten.]

p

*Suggested simplification:

AB 2008

D.C. al Fine
[♩ = c.96]

POLONOISE in F
[Allegretto]

[♩ = c.80]

MENUET in F

18

mf [*non legato*]

Fine

★Suggested simplification:

All dynamics are editorial.

AB 2008

D.C. al Fine

[♩ = c.108]

ANDANTE in G

19

All dynamics are editorial.   AB 2008   [♩ = c.69]

ALLEGRO in D minor

20

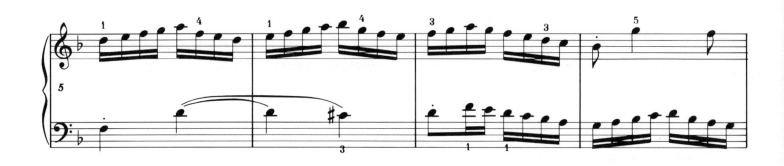

★B♭ in the original.

All slurs and dynamics are editorial.

AB 2008

[♩ = c.84]

ANDANTE in E

21

Fine

VILLANELLA in B flat

[Allegretto scherzando]

f [non legato]

p

f [leggiero]

p   *f*

mf   ★   *p*

★ Only G appoggiatura in source.

All slurs are editorial.

[♩ = c.72]

ALLEGRO IN B flat

23

33

All slurs and dynamics are editorial.

AB 2008

[𝅗𝅥 = c.60]

ALLEGRO in G

24

f [sempre leggiero]

[non legato]

dim.

mf

mp

p

p

mf

mf

cresc. 2da volta: dim.

*D in original.

All slurs and dynamics are editorial.

AB 2008

ADAGIO in C minor

25

mf [cantabile]

cresc.

p

f

mf

dim.

mp

[♪ = c.92]

MENUET in A

40

(9)

Reproduced and printed by Halstan & Co. Ltd., Amersham, Bucks., England